The World Under the Water

by Ted Jamison

illustrated by Eulala Conner

Harcourt

Orlando   Boston   Dallas   Chicago   San Diego

Visit *The Learning Site!*

www.harcourtschool.com

When you live on an island, you can learn a lot about the water that surrounds it. I live in Hawaii, and I've learned a lot about the world under the water here.

The sky is so blue. The sun warms the land and also the ocean around the islands.

I have been snorkeling in the
ocean since I was very small. All
you really need is a mask and
breathing tube.

4

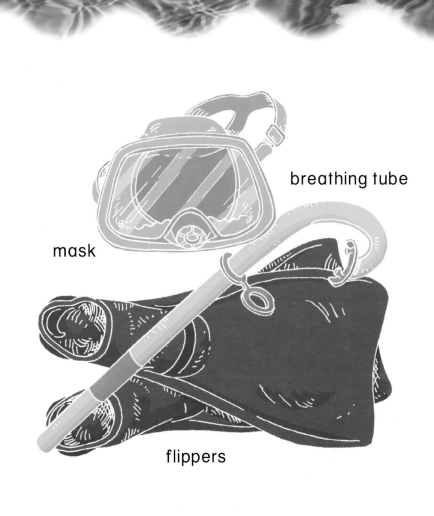

mask

breathing tube

flippers

If you want to use fins, they help you swim faster.

It helps to get some good
information about which beaches
are best for snorkeling.

We asked at a dive store for clues about where to go. We were given details about the kinds of fish we might see.

"Never snorkel alone," the store owner told us. "Oceans are very beautiful, but you must stay safe. Snorkeling is a lot of fun. It won't disappoint you."

When we arrived at the beach,
we got ready to go. I thought we
might scare the fish with our
funny masks and fins!

The world under the water was
amazing! The fish came so close.
I wanted to get closer and stroke
them, but they are too fast!

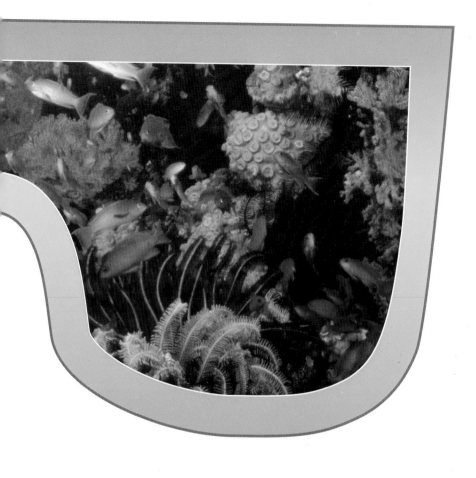

That first time, I swam at the surface of the water and held my dad's hand. It isn't hard to swim with those big fins on.

I saw another world under the
water. Ocean life is beautiful.

The fish came right up to me!

We fed the fish some lettuce
and peas. This is good fish food.

The water was warm and I wanted to stay and play. Dad had to forcibly pull me out!

Now I am an underwater guide.
I know the names of the fish and
creatures that live here. I take
new explorers out to see the ocean
that is part of my home.